IT'S A CAT'S LIFE—
AND DON'T YOU WISH
YOU WERE LEADING IT!

What is it like to rise from the slums to superstardom?

What is it like to have millions of dollars riding on the twitch of your whiskers?

What is it like to have your pick of the world's most purr-fect mates—including that wild white Persian, Ethel?

What is it like to come between Dyan Cannon and Burt Reynolds on Hollywood's most uninhibited set?

What, in short, is it like to be

MORRIS

As Morris says, you only have nine lives—and you might as well get the most out of all of them!

MORRIS

by Mary Daniels

A DELL BOOK

To Roxana

Published by
DELL PUBLISHING CO., INC.
1 Dag Hammarskjold Plaza
New York, New York 10017

First Dell printing—November 1975
Second Dell printing—December 1975
Third Dell printing—February 1976

MORRIS

"Obviously this is an elite typewriter
if I'm telling my life story on it."

INTRODUCTION

"Hmph!" said Morris when I told him I was going to write his biography. "I thought I was getting Norman Mailer."

Of course, one expects the world's most finicky feline to be fussy about his Boswell too. But *Norman Mailer!* He probably didn't even like cats, let alone consider them people!

I knew *I* had to be the one to write Morris' fabulous rats-to-riches story, and I was determined to convince him.

I spent hours in quaint, creaky libraries reading rare tomes on cat psychology.

I sprayed myself with that catnip you're supposed to put on toys.

I even went so far as to offer him some payola—a shoe box full of white mice. He declined, with some regret, saying he'd like to accept but he was in enough trouble already with the IRS, which had a heck of a time trying to figure out his taxes as it was, since he accepted his income in cat food and catnip mice.

The pressure and the tension mounted.

As a result of all my stories about him in the *Chicago Tribune* and *Cats Magazine,* I was getting lots of mail with questions on details of his life that family newspapers couldn't print. His fans were intrigued, and I knew a tell-all book would be a smash hit. My publisher called me every day to see if I'd made any progress in getting Morris to put his famous paw print on a contract.

But nothing I tried seemed to work. I began to doubt he'd ever give in.

Then one day while I was contemplating the vagaries of fortune, I happened to catch a commercial Morris made in which he writes a testimonial letter to 9-Lives, thanking them for a tasty new product.

I remembered his mentioning once that it was *his* favorite commercial. I know most cats enjoy typing. But there was really something special about the way Morris was composing that letter.

The very next time I saw him I asked, "Morris, do you have any secret ambitions? Is there anything, with all your success, you feel you'd still like to do?"

Sure enough . . . (heh-heh).

He told me he thought he could also make the world's most finicky writer. (I suspect there's some rivalry between him and that other four-footed world-famous author, star of a comic strip.)

I jumped right in and asked him why he didn't tell his own story then. I would just help him with the . . . ah . . . retyping, since he is a little slow.

Not long after that I caught him wearing his turtleneck kitty sweater and sitting at the typewriter, batting out items he said *had* to go in *his* book. (He wrote all the chapter headings before he got bored and a little tired and decided to let me help him with the rest, which I'd banked on anyway.)

We had a big argument about the title, which Morris wanted to call "Any Cat Can," but I never heard anything about Norman Mailer again.

1
"A FUNNY THING HAPPENED
TO ME ON THE WAY TO
MY NEXT LIFE . . ."

In true show-biz tradition, and in keeping with the legend of a cat having nine lives, just when it appeared his luck had run out and this was the end, it all began for Morris.

Things certainly didn't look promising. There were, in fact, only twenty minutes to go before the Big Sleep when animal talent scout Bob Martwick wandered in the door of the Hinsdale Humane Society, where the big orange tiger was being held.

As Martwick supplied most of the Chicago television and photography studios with four-legged actors, he was now looking for a very special one, for a rather tough assignment. It was a rather large audition.

It was spring and the cages were full at this animal shelter in an affluent southwestern suburb of Chicago. Strays were being rounded up every day, and one batch was quickly "dispatched" to make room for more in the cages of the Kitty Room at the shelter.

(Like most places of its kind, this shelter tried to do its best by the animals which passed through its doors, and find them new homes, but circumstances would force them to resort to this sort of thing.)

There were a few poor devils, scroungy and near-basket cases from life on the bum, but there were also plenty of good-looking types, who, like the big orange tiger, had by a twist of fate been placed on the edge of disaster.

Bob Martwick's eye, however, was drawn to the orange tiger, he remembers, not only because of the cat's imposing appearance, but because, despite his precarious situation, he still acted as if he had a deed to the place, rubbing his cheeks against the bars as if it were the most important thing in the world to do.

Martwick took the orange cat out of his cage and placed him on the cement floor. The big cat just stood at his feet and looked him over, never giving a thought to running away, as most cats would have done.

The talent scout knew he needed a cat who would not rattle easily. He dropped an empty tin food plate on the floor, and the orange tiger just gave a sort of "so what" look to the clang. Martwick would find later that this cat, unlike others, had a nervous system made of thin, tubular diamonds.

Then he "tested him for affection" and patted the big M-marked head. The orange cat responded, brushing his head against the man's pants leg.

Martwick decided the cat just might do for what he had in mind.

"I had a sense of something," Martwick would say later. "I didn't know if he was a star, but I knew he was different."

It was a tremendously dramatic beginning.

Of course, Morris sees it all differently. He says Martwick *never* picked him. He picked Martwick. And he really looked *him* over. He had already turned down two other prospects, he says, in the two previous days. (Little did Martwick know what he was being picked for—to become valet, drama coach, and trainer of the world's first feline superstar.)

And Morris was never worried. He says if Martwick hadn't walked in just then, something else would have happened; what, he doesn't exactly know, but he's confident it would have.

Besides, he says, he hadn't used up anywhere near his nine lives. He had plenty more to go.

Morris even claims that when Martwick carried him out of the animal shelter to his car and said, "Boy, are you Lucky," giving him an interim name, Morris had merely answered, "We've got to stop meeting like this."

2
"A MATTRESS IS MY SPRINGBOARD
TO THE BIG TIME"

As they left the Hinsdale shelter together, neither human nor feline knew it as yet, but the cat in the orange-striped jailbird pajamas, whose life had been bought for a mere five dollars, was already on his way to becoming the most famous member of his species in the world.

Yet it was nothing glamorous like a governor's pardon that had saved his life, but a photographer's order to find a cat to pose for some commercials for a leading mattress firm. It shows how often in life the best of luck comes in the most homely wrappings.

The cat made his first trip to the Chicago Loop down a crowded expressway smelly with car smoke. He then got what was to be the first look of many at the inside of a film studio.

"Weird," thought the cat, *"weird,"* as his new friend made firm gestures he knew meant he was to sit still in a window he also knew was phony. Not only that, but the whole room he was looking into was phony. The gold-papered walls went only so far and so high. There was a bed in the middle, but it had no sheets, even though two humans, a man and a woman, were on it, pretending to be asleep under the blazing lights. All the while a whole lot of other humans were scurrying around like a nest of mice in the dark edges around the sideless end of the "room."

The cat was giving heavy consideration to strolling over to the end of the mattress and having himself a good scratch. It had been a long time since he'd had one, long before he'd been captured and put into that dumb place, and the mattress did look like a scratchable one. But just then some kook began aiming two hoses at the window—the cat guessed this was to pretend it was ugh! pouring rain, right on him!

He got the picture. He was supposed to sit there, getting drenched on the windowsill, waiting for the human on the bed to come over and let him in through the window.

Hmmhh! thought the cat. He'd certainly had enough practice doing that in real life. So he did what his new friend seemed to want from him. Compared to what he had just been through, it was no fur lost, as cats say. And he really liked the attention he was getting, as he could tell everyone was looking at him, rather than at the humans on the bed.

There were eighteen takes, for both still ads and a television commercial. After the last, everyone applauded—for the orange cat. It was a taste of what was yet to come.

Martwick plucked the cat from the phony windowsill where he still sat. The man seemed very happy with him, as did everyone else. They talked to him, stroked his head, and offered him the best parts of their sandwiches.

"Humans will eat anything," mused the cat, as he sampled this and that and finally cleaned his chops.

The mattress commercial would be a modest success, but later when the cat was very famous and had a big name, his future employers (possessive, as some humans are known to be) would go right up the wall at the very mention of it and would try to buy up any old copies that were still around.

The cat himself would never be ashamed of an honest day's work. "I was broke and needed the job," he would explain later.

"You'd think I'd posed in a basket with a ribbon on for a calendar," he would grump at his agency's attitude.

The orange cat went home with Bob Martwick to what he discovered was a pleasant place in the country, except for one fact. It was a place where many dogs (we hate to even say it here) came and went daily. This, to be sure, did not sit too well with him. But there was no other cat in charge, so he quickly assumed the position and decided he might even stay on.

The man, Martwick, steadily referred to the orange tiger as "Lucky," because of his narrow escape from the Big Sleep.

For some time things went on in a peaceful and uneventful way. Then, about six months later, Martwick received another call from a large advertising agency in the big city, Leo Burnett USA. They said they were "putting out a cat call." They needed a representative feline to just sort of *be* in a commercial they were creating for a client, Star-Kist Foods, Inc., which wanted to promote its 9-Lives cat food.

"They just wanted a cat, a nice-looking cat that would eat well," Martwick remembers. Lucky certainly qualified on both counts. And he did have this unusual charisma. Even the scars from his pre-acting days—the two small slashes above his left eye, the ears notched like Billy the Kid's gun, the tic-tac-toe crosses on the nose—were no detriment, but lent him a special rakish appeal.

So into a large metal carrying case, one designed for dogs, but the only one the orange tiger could fit into comfortably, and down the expressway for the second time into the big city went our hero.

At this point, as Lucky arrived in the conference room of the advertising agency, the director had looked at two or three dozen assorted felines in his attempt at cat-casting. He had been cursed at in cat innu-

14

"Clark Gable and I may have a lot in common, but it sure doesn't include feet."

merable times, he would never get the hair from his wardrobe, and Band-Aids still covered a minor scratch or two. He was not feeling very hopeful.

As for what happened next, to this day Bob Martwick, a very honest man, shakes his head and disclaims any responsibility for what the orange cat was about to do: "I don't know how he did it! He was astounding!"

Martwick had just leaned down to slip the catch on the door of Lucky's traveling kennel. The big cat bounded out, leaped onto the polished conference table, and strode purposefully down its length right up to the director.

"This looks like the Clark Gable of cats," said the director, who couldn't help being impressed and just happened to be the guy giving out the job.

"Any previous acting experience?" he asked, eyes narrowing, trying to gather a little job-giver's cynicism about him.

Martwick told him how Lucky had gone through "a test by water" in his first acting job and had never flinched, and that, for a cat, he was remarkably cooperative and relatively nontemperamental on the set.

The director rubbed his chin and said, "Well, let's try a screen test."

(Reflecting on that day, Morris would comment: "A cat who doesn't walk into a conference room as if he owns it never will.")

When the director saw the "dailies," the footage of film shot of the orange tiger, he immediately called his most agile writers and told them to rework the whole commercial so that what was originally a walk-on part was expanded along the same lines to become a starring role.

Then, shortly before the orange tiger went in front of the cameras to play his new role, his writers decided the new star had to have a new name. "Lucky" just wouldn't do.

He needed a name that had a personal ring to it, because this cat obviously *was* a person. The name had to have some dignity and prestige.

Because he has the kind of personality which invites deference, the team asked the orange tiger what name *he* would like.

He tried to tell them his real cat name. The closest they could make it out to be was Mmmrrrsss, so they believed he was telling them he would like Morris as his new professional name.

The orange cat sort of shrugged to himself. Well, he was really glad to be rid of Lucky, even though he had never answered to it. It was embarrassingly doggish and rather common. Morris was an improvement and actually very, very close to his real cat name. After all, Tony Curtis used to be called Bernie Schwartz before he became a big star, right?

The cat had a way of looking serenely at the things that happened to him. Even the bad days and the narrow escape. Now they would work for him and loom large in his legend.

Years later, when the orange tiger was very, very famous, many people from distant parts of the country where he had never set paw would call long distance and claim him.

But then he would put on his "Eat Your Heart Out, Former Owner" look and be glad folks felt guilty and even greedy about him. They would think twice before tossing out another cat and putting it into the situation he'd been in. Now, though, there was work to be done, and he sauntered onto the television set, tail describing a lazy *s,* as if it were a balmy evening and he were out to do the town, and not at all as if he had an important message to deliver to catdom.

3
"THAT CROOKED GRIN OF MINE . . ."

When Morris first entered American homes in 1969, it was love at first sight. He became one of the few true overnight successes in the business.

For those who may have been so unfortunate as to miss it, we re-create that first starring role here, for it was the trigger of an important etho-sociological phenomenon.

"9-Lives Presents Morris" ran the credits, and as they fade, the scene opens on tranquil domesticity.

A large orange tiger cat is snoozing away, face to the camera, in an overstuffed brown velvet chair that handsomely sets off his incendiary complexion. A few healthy snores can be heard.

Then an off-camera female voice calls, "Here, Sweety, come, Sweety." Obviously well meant, it nevertheless rudely awakens our sleeping protagonist.

He yawns widely, looking somewhat rumpled, as if an army of gerbils has just marched through his mouth in their bare feet. He shakes his handsome head and comments wryly, "Ugh! Sweety! My name is Morris! Does she have to call me Sweety?"

"Here's something new for din-din," continues the syrupy, domestic, but insistent voice, somewhere between Martha Mitchell and Mrs. Portnoy.

"Hmph! Din-din. I'll eat when I'm ready," our hero asserts his masculinity. Morris begins to arise, stretch, and unrumple himself.

"First I want to check the weather," he says, putting his big front paws up on the back of the chair and avidly peering through the gauzy curtains of a window.

"I'm stepping out tonighhhtt," he sings rakishly. Instantly we know this is a man of the world, an Errol Flynn, no henpecked armchair sitter. He will do exactly as he pleases.

"Come on, it's new 9-Lives Super Supper. It's good for fussy eaters like you," insists the female voice.

"Is that so! We'll see about that," says Morris. He jumps down from the chair and saunters into the kitchen through swinging louvered doors (evidence is piling up that this is a cat of some taste and distinction, as apparent from his choice of home).

There is a brief moment of comic relief as the doors swing closed after him and pinch his short, orange-barred tail. He gives a small start and complains, "Ouch, that smarts!" pauses a moment, and then continues on his debonair way.

"Now, what's so super about 9-Lives Super Supper?" He jumps on top of a kitchen stool in front of a can placed on the counter. From just in back of his intelligent ears you see him reading the ingredients: "Hmmm! Fish, chicken parts, meat by-products, liver, and kidney!"

A feminine hand takes the can and whirs it through the opener. "See, Sweety, all your favorite num-nums . . . in one can," she says.

The camera then pans to Morris, who is eating with great gusto. "Say, with food like this . . . smack [he licks his chops] . . . you can call me anything . . . but . . . smack . . . call me." He looks up as if speaking directly to the woman off-screen, then turns to the food again as an announcer's voice delivers the final spiel: "New 9-Lives Super Supper, fish, chicken parts, meat by-products, liver, and kidney. The natural com-

"Cleanliness is next to finickiness."

"Little dum-dum . . ."

bination of five natural, ah, num-nums."

The message is clear: "I am a cat. I go first class, until luxury class comes along. The only way to win me is with the best of everything."

Filmed on location in Chicago in May, 1968, that one-minute opus ran for the first time in that same city on May 5, 1969. A thirty-second version ran nationally shortly afterward on June 19, 1969.

(If you're wondering what took so long, a search was on for the perfect voice for Morris, which, as his contract read, he had sole right to approve. He says at first they offered him "inappropriate" voices, one which even sounded like Woody Allen's! And another which was rough, like Stanley Kowalski's. At last a West Coast actor, who prefers to remain anonymous, as he doesn't want to be "voice"-cast, turned up, with one that is an exact translation of Morris' own. A sort of George Sanders stance. "Ask any of my cat friends if that doesn't sound like me," says our star, who gave his immediate approval.)

The brand of num-nums which Morris was touting immediately began to disappear off supermarket shelves as if it were programmed to self-destruct five minutes after it left the carton.

Semi-trailers full of fan mail began arriving at the home offices of Star-Kist Foods in California.

A surprised but thrilled cat-food company suddenly realized it had a yellow and orange gold mine on its hands.

When told of the success of his first starring role, Morris just sat and calmly cleaned a paw. When you've got it, you don't have to flaunt it, he seemed to say.

Some time passed while another appropriate vehicle was secured. Writers were put to work, and toward the end of 1969 a number of short films were made.

There was "Girl Friend," co-starring Ethel the White Persian. Who will forget those thrilling lines, "Ethel baby, you are something else"? He leaves her, though, in the end, for a can of tuna.

22

Then there was also "More Morris," in which he delivers those classic lines, "The cat who doesn't act finicky soon loses control of his owner," lines destined to be emblazoned in the minds of all the felines watching at home.

There were "Doll Buggy" and "Tea Party" in which he had a little human co-star, great all-time hits. More and more homes posted a Morris "scout" in front of the TV set, to alert the rest of the family when a Morris drama appeared.

In "Morris and Albert" he again had a co-star, this one a male feline. Little Albert, an eight-week-old striped gray kitten, plays the role of the houseguest who comes to spend the week and upsets Morris' carefully secured life-style.

"Little dum-dum," Morris calls Albert in the film, because "she says din-din and he's off like a shot. Dum-dum hasn't learned that the cat who doesn't act finicky . . . loses control of his owner."

"Hey! Look at that kid eat," notices Morris as Little Albert digs in. "I'd better get over there myself before it's all gone."

Morris admits at the end of the story that Albert, when it comes to choice of food, isn't so dumb after all.

Things were not so rosy on the set, however. There were stories of dissension between the by now firmly established star and the young co-star, who reportedly tried to steal scenes.

Little Albert is supposed to have said, "It was like sharing a plate with Genghis Khan," but we must take into account his youth and suppose some sour grapes on his part.

There was another film in which Morris was supposed to bring home a buddy for dinner, old black and white Harry.

"He didn't like the buddy and clobbered him," remembers Martwick. Harry was never invited to return.

Subsequently, less and less co-starring roles were created, which suited Morris just fine.

It wasn't that he felt threatened. It was just the temperament of genius asserting itself. He is a perfectionist and demands perfection of others.

After half a dozen or so successful roles, Morris asked for a raise and got a lifetime contract. He was also made an honorary member of his company's board of directors and was given complete veto power over any new flavor of cat food that did not suit his taste. He sat in on sales meetings as well.

Other cat-food companies began to feel the pinch. They scouted the country for feline talent to put up against Morris.

Unaware of who Morris' handler was, one company exec called Bob Martwick one day and asked him to find them a cat to star in one of their commercials. "And don't bring me any orange tigers," he growled before banging down the phone.

Things quickly became competitive in the cat-food commercial game, with challengers launching new advertising campaigns in order to place or show.

Cats did the rumba and the samba and a version of the Radio City Rockettes chorus line. They sent their owners on missions impossible to find things to tempt their palates. They consorted with their jungle cousins. They played a nonspeaking Scarlett O'Hara, Kitty from "Gunsmoke," Lorelei Lee from *Gentlemen Prefer Blondes*. One story line even pointed out rather obviously and against the grain of all legend that cats have only three lives instead of nine.

But somehow it was always the humans who had to carry the acting load, and this was not what the public wanted to see, or rather, they could see *that* anytime they wanted.

No one could come up with a feline star who had the Brando impact of our orange-furred friend. And no one else could create an image to rival his, which somehow hit a special target.

"You with the dog food, outta line!"

In trying to analyze the situation, critics in tall towns who had nothing better to do wrote long columns about how there was a subtle sexual sell to the Morris commercials, and that Freud was selling cat food. Morris, they said, was really a symbol of an erring husband, and his wife was keeping him at home by feeding him tuna, and other silly things like that.

In order to set the record straight, we decided to ask a highly regarded psychologist to give her opinion of whether or not there was some libido in the woodpile.

Perhaps Dr. Maria Piers, Dean of the famed Erikson Institute for Early Education in Chicago, will have to be excused if she does not seem to have all her professional objectivity about her in this case. Asked to comment on our superstar, she smiled and said she was aware of who he was. She had watched him perform on TV and had "sat there entranced."

Could she analyze his appeal?

She referred to what she called "a rather elaborate theory by Konrad Lorenz," the great father of the science of ethology, which studies the parallels in the behavior patterns of both two- and four-legged animals.

Dr. Lorenz had talked to Dr. Piers personally, she said, about this particular theory, which holds that "certain animals share certain features with the human infant . . . the full cheeks . . . certain body features . . ."

Which means we can not only relate to them easily as humans but as nonthreatening ones.

We explained to her that Morris' singular charisma doesn't merely spin out cat lovers but also grabs dog devotees, rodent raisers, and even people who don't care much for other people.

Because of Morris, cats across the country now feel free to do their own thing and feel appreciated for being themselves. No longer do they have to try to live up to the image of that other, supposedly superior race, the canine.

26

Folks not only treated the cats they knew better, but went out and tried to be friends with one for the first time, thanks to Morris.

Why are they so bowled over?

"Because we can identify with Morris' having to put up with this other person upon whom he is dependent," explained Dr. Piers. " 'Here I am,' he says, 'superior, brilliant, but I have to try to get along with this dummy because my next meal may be coming from her.' "

(Cat owners love it as Morris confirms what they've suspected all along about the way their own cats talk about them behind their backs.)

"Cats," she concluded, "have a justified disdain for people, which we share with them."

We took this analysis to Morris, who reviewed it with as much attention as if it were a mousehole from which he'd just seen a pink wriggly nose peek out.

But he finally stood up and stalked away, his only comment a flick of his tail and an "Actually, I owe it all to my crooked grin."

4
"HOW THEY 'MAKE' ME DO ALL THAT STUFF"
plus
TEN FABULOUS TIPS ON HOW ANY CAT
CAN BE A SUPERSTAR IN HIS OR HER OWN HOME

The camera continued its love affair with our hero, and it was not long before his remarkable talent received official recognition.

In July, 1973, the American Humane Association nominated Morris for its twenty-third annual presentation of the Patsy awards—the animal kingdom's equivalent of the Oscar and the Emmy. Morris spruced himself up and, unlike certain human stars we will not name, flew off to Hollywood to attend the Patsy ceremonies with dignity and class.

Emcees Betty White, an actress herself, and Allen Ludden introduced the four-footed actors and explained their acting credits. The competition could really be said to be tooth and nail.

Just before the taping of the show began, Bear, a stunning cougar who had appeared on NBC-TV's "Ghost Story," let professional jealousy get the best of him and tried to do some personal eliminating by jumping on the back of Ott, a black stallion who was hoping for a Patsy for his performance on "Bonanza." Fortunately, Ott's feelings were hurt more than anything else, but he and Bear will not be invited to the same party for a long time to come.

"Hmph! Giving a Patsy to a rat
is ridiculous."

Major, the lion who had starred in Walt Disney Productions' *Napoleon and Samantha,* apparently had had a little too much of something before the ceremony and kept roaring about how he was the "King of Beasts" and for that reason alone should be given a Patsy.

Six Doberman pinschers, five of whom had worked in the Rosamond Productions' *Doberman Gang,* and one from MGM's *They Only Kill Their Masters,* lent a touch of sleek elegance to the nominee lineup.

Shortie, an elephant standing in, or rather nervously swaying in, for a buddy named Bimbo, who was on location but had lumbered creditably through an episode of "Gunsmoke," was bothered by the presence of another animal star, Ben the Rat.

Ben, star of the Bing Crosby Productions film named for him, was, in turn, a bundle of nerves when he saw Major and Morris. Ben couldn't even be calmed down when he was given a Patsy for his work in feature films.

And when a moment later Morris was given his Patsy for "outstanding performance in a TV commercial" (unfortunately these folks didn't realize Morris' commercials *are* feature films), the first time a Patsy was given in this category, Ben ducked into the pocket of his owner-trainer, Moe Di Sesso. When one of the emcees tastelessly referred to Morris' rats-to-riches background, the pocket quivered vigorously.

Morris decided this was not a night to think of the past, however, and he was at his most urbane throughout the ceremony, a credit to his kind who were watching avidly back home.

(Gossip columnists later reported that Lassie, retired from Patsy competition by his owner, Rudd Weatherwax, because of having won so many times previously, *he said,* for his female impersonation act, had been sitting in one of the front rows of the audience and had howled when Morris received his award. There is a news photo which does lend credence to this rumor.)

It was a big moment for Morris.

Our star was pressed for interviews. Once again, the ubiquitous question—how did he do it?

How was he induced to do his incredible, subtle acting feats, when most cats cannot ever be convinced to do anything?

Morris, however, remained unavailable for comment and retired to the seclusion of his country estate. It has not been until now, in the preparation of this book, that he has decided to reveal some of his techniques.

"I cooperate, but not too much . . . A cat who is too cooperative soon loses control of his handler."

Martwick, his drama coach, is very cautious himself about taking too much credit for Morris' success. He will refer to Morris as "workable," but never by that other, doggish word, "trainable."

Morris is conscious of the fact that he is the quintessential model for a nation's cats and has drawn a fine line between working to uplift the cat image and compromising his own catly integrity.

He is able to follow a script in an extraordinarily exact way.

"People think we shoot thousands and thousands of feet of film to get what we want," Martwick has said. "We don't. We go right by the story board."

The technique is simple. Morris belongs to the John Wayne school of acting. He is himself at all times— merely transferring his own personality onto the screen.

He denies rumors he once studied the Stanislavsky method in New York. Why do that, when he's already deep into his only role as Everycat? Of course, his ability to perform boldly in front of cameras and even live audiences *does* make him different from most other cats.

But I feel he enjoys being a star so much, it overrides normal feline resistance to doing anything vaguely resembling human desires.

Photos taken at the Santa
Monica Cat Club Show—a
benefit for Pet Pride. Credit:
*Pet Pride and the Santa
Monica Cat Club*

"We can do a commercial in a day," says Martwick. Usually a "bank" of them is accumulated, then Morris can be free to leave town for publicity tours.

Does he ever watch his own work?

Martwick says yes. Once when they were on the road and in a hotel room, the television was on. "9-Lives Presents" flashed across the screen, and Morris, who was resting on the edge of the bed, picked up his head and looked at the set when he heard his name. He watched with some attention for several seconds, then went back to catch some "z's."

Does he know he's famous?

"I think he does," says his handler. He thinks Morris just puts on a special air when he's being the star. As his biographer, I would have to second that.

By now it's well known that Morris prefers working alone, as far as other cats are concerned. But asked to comment on the humans with whom he's co-starred, he merely shrugged. After some purposeful insistence on my part (as I have long suspected, he is not quite as misanthropic as he feels it is necessary to display in his roles), he admitted he "rather liked" that little girl who had dressed him in a bonnet and called him Mrs. White in "Tea Party."

A reel of "outtakes," parts of a Morris filming which had hit the cutting room floor, had once fallen into my hands by accidental means, and I was stunned when I had had it run through a projector.

He had really *carried on* with that little girl, showering her with all sorts of attention, helping her with her cues, going along with the whole idea of the tea party, even getting lost in the role, sticking his nose in the tiny china cup in order to make her giggle, playing the fool, none of which was on the story board at all.

No reporters had been allowed on the set, and the whole thing was hushed up, but I suspect it's an important clue to his past.

I've also noticed when he's giving his trademark greeting, the famous Morris head-bump to fans, adorable little misses get extra snugglings. Did he once have one of his own?

He is rather amused to have a "tuna company" of his own and, although money means nothing to a cat, he thoroughly enjoys some of the status symbols that success brings.

He has a collapsible Vuitton litter box, and says he doesn't mind riding in chauffeured limousines at all. "It sure beats [bleep] out of the humane society truck," he has been known to remark.

In order to insure that his work filters down all the way to where it should, Morris himself has sponsored an acting award of sorts—"The Morris," which is given to the Best Household Pet at cat shows all over the country.

While I have been busy sorting out all of the above information, Morris has been preparing a favorite project of his own. Someday he hopes to do a full feature-length film on the subject, but right now he's limited it to ten fabulous tips on how any cat can make himself a nominee for the Morris award.

Here they are. Since much of his work (he works slowly but carefully) is in rough draft and much had still to be translated directly from the feline (which he lapses into whenever he wants to be exact in expressing himself), I have had to work with it some.

1. From the first moment, act as if you are the main attraction. If you are not, soon you will be.

2. Make dramatic entrances. Never let a human close a door on you. Fling it open before you. A very good entrance is to slither into the living room and dissolve into a languid odalisque or Burt Reynolds (whichever applies) position in the middle of the carpet. Pick a color which sets off your own.

It is sometimes effective to stretch out on top of places you know you really shouldn't—such as the breakfast table, the refrigerator . . . The sense of the forbidden heightens excitement.

"You handsome devil, you."

Sitting on top of reading matter is also a good way to be "in the news."

3. Don't always be available. This speaks for itself. A cat who is always available cannot keep his owner guessing.

4. Expect the best of everything. This is the cardinal rule.

5. Grooming *is* everything. A cat who does not look his or her best cannot expect the best. Preening is permissible. Remember, your beauty is incomparable— great writers have said it—but don't be just another pretty body. Know how to use it.

6. Be sensuous. That silk scarf and that fur coat are there for you to lie on. Be sparing in your display of affections, no matter what you *really* feel. Always play hard to get. The idea is to keep the balance of feelings on *their* side. If you feel you *must* make a display, be dramatic about it always.

Try slithering up and making an attempt to brush against your human, but miss by about three inches. This has the effect of near tantalizing them to death. Limit the liberties to be taken in their offering their esteem to you.

7. Never, *never* allow yourself to be upstaged. If there is a—oh, we hate to say it—dog living with you, one most effective way to put him or her in his place, that will get you into the least trouble and cost the least effort, is to show him a tolerant affection. Your human will be so wiped out by this, that you have done this for *him,* that if Fang dares to step out of line once with you, it will be his paws out on the patio rather than yours.

If it's another cat you have to compete with, you are on your own, says Morris, and may the best cat win.

If it's a human baby which comes into your household and vies for attention, don't worry about it. Time will go by and you will have another slave.

8. Be seen in all the right places—a sunlit window, the top of the sofa, the middle of the bed atop the pil-

lows, next to a statue of a cat, etc. You get the idea. This may overlap a bit with 1, 6, and 7.

9. Practice your charisma. Smile when your human comes home. (Then when you don't, you can get whatever you want.) Go to the door several minutes before his or her car rounds the corner and comes up the drive, so another member of the family will report how mysteriously omniscient and lovestruck you are. Humans are pushovers for this. Do little human things every now and then. Pick up a piece of food in your paw. Pat your human's face gently with a paw to wake him.

10. Last, never be too eager about anything. Attitude is everything. Always let it be subtly understood that, if things are not up to your standards, you know you can get a better lifetime contract somewhere else.

5
"MY STAND-IN DOES <u>NOT</u> STAND OUT"

Being a great star is not all creamed gravy and tuna. There are problems, and not all of them are as simple as whether or not to use whisker wax on TV.

The closer you get to the peak, the less room there is to stand and the more jostling there is of egos. And when you are at the very top, there is always someone just below you as eager as you were to get there, and breathing hot and heavy on your tail.

Morris was used to being continually challenged, but it posed no real threat. "Imitation is the finickiest form of flattery," he was heard to say.

But he never expected to be threatened by plots from within his own organization!

Of course, the staff didn't look at the situation that way. In the middle of 1972, they decided to hold a Lookalike Contest which would serve two purposes—it would be fun and would make many people happy.

When Morris heard about it, he was as impassive as a log. He decided just to go along with the ludicrous idea. After all, the idea of another cat coming close to resembling him couldn't possibly bother him. Was it his fault if humans weren't aware that each and every cat has a biological obligation to be unique? Morris just crossed it off as another of those bizarre things—well-meaning but ignorant—that humans try to bring off for obscure reasons of their own.

That following fall he didn't particularly balk when his sheepskin sleeping rug was packed into his carrying case and he was off on tour. He appeared on television shows and granted newspaper interviews in a nine-state area in the northeastern part of the country, patiently telling the public about his Lookalike Contest and politely inviting people to send in photos of their candidates.

In just a few weeks there was a vigorous response of seven hundred entries.

However, as the judges would find, not too many would really look like Morris.

There were even a few photos of black cats with attached letters saying: "I know he doesn't look like Morris, but inside he *is* Morris."

A few of the photos sent in were of a pair of red eyes glowing out from the dark space under a chair, or of an indistinguishable blur crossing a room. One had to take the word of the humans who sent in the entries that these camera-shy contestants really did look like Morris.

The whole batch was culled by the distinguished panel of judges, including Dr. Les Fisher, director of Chicago's Lincoln Park Zoo; Dr. Wallace Eagle, Morris' personal physician, and Bob Martwick.

After much deliberation, the judges chose a five-year-old tomcat named Gilly, owned by Mr. and Mrs. John H. Quimby of Boston, Massachusetts, as the grand winner. The Quimbys were notified and were invited to Chicago with Gilly for an all-expenses-paid whirlwind weekend on the town early in December.

A long, black, chauffeur-driven limousine carried a load of Morris' personal public relations people, a somewhat skeptical Bob Martwick, one privileged member of the entire press corps (me), and Morris himself toward O'Hare Airport to meet Gilly.

Morris was in good humor. After greeting me

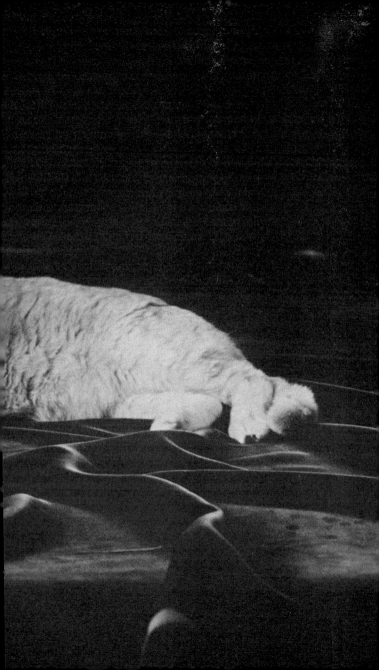

warmly, he went back up on the top of the black leather front seat and watched critically every move the chauffeur made.

(To this day I feel that he misunderstood what was going on. I don't think he realized he would ever have to *see* his supposed Lookalike. I don't think he minded that one existed, as long as he didn't have to look at the guy in cat.)

Anyway, the airlines had arranged for Morris and Gilly to have their big meeting in their own pressroom at O'Hare Airport. Everyone just sort of shuffled into it to wait out the last few minutes before the Quimbys' arrival.

Morris began to check out his surroundings with all the diligent klutz of a Columbo. He took a few nips out of all the plants in the room, scattered beloved knick-knacks on all the desks, tipped over a cup of water offered to him, then ransacked the coffeepot-and-cups table for any stray Danish crumbs.

Anyone else would say he was nervous. But to watch Martwick's jaw pull in tight against his chin, I suspected he knew worse.

Other members of the press, including a TV cameraman, arrived to record this historic meeting, and suddenly there were the Quimbys, carrying a cat case, rounding the corner.

Mr. Quimby put Gilly's case down and opened it, drawing out a big bargelloed amber tom who, judging from the scabs and scars on his face, probably was the ward boss in his own neighborhood.

There was a general chorus of exclamations and critiques as the cameras clicked and whirred. Martwick himself, the most qualified judge, admitted that the resemblance wasn't too bad. The coats were by the same label furrier. But there were some differences about the nose and jowls.

Then Morris himself decided to give his opinion. With a growl, he whipped out a right to Gilly's head.

42

WANTED

cats that look like
MORRIS the 9·Lives TV Star

"Imitation is the finickiest form
of flattery."

(A quick-thinking member of the PR staff stepped in front of the cameras just at that moment.)

Martwick, who sometimes finds himself in the role of referee around his feline friend, coaxed Morris back to his side of the desk and decided it was time to proceed to lunch.

The limo at last arrived at the famed Ambassador East Hotel. This was the stopping place for celebs and home of the Pump Room, which *Life* Magazine once called the most exotic restaurant in the country.

The two cats went up to the front desk and Gilly registered by paw print while Morris looked on as flashbulbs exploded.

Now this, please remember, is the place where you're very liable to see Chuck Connors, or William Friedkin, or Lauren Bacall transiting through the lobby.

Since the hotel's staff is so accustomed to celebrities, they don't usually twitch a muscle at famous faces. But bellhops, guests, and even back-room reservations clerks came out to smile and greet the two cats.

"Which one is Morris?" inquired a top FBI man, and he picked his likely suspect.

"Don't be silly," admonished a famous woman foreign correspondent. "It's the one with the crooked grin!" she detected correctly.

Leaving the lobby thoroughly astir, the two cats were escorted directly to the Pump Room. A forewarned maître d' had piled plump white pillows in the ultimate of status seats, Booth One. (A list of the fannies which have rested on that white leather banquette would make a Who's Who.)

Service, as good as it usually is in the Pump Room, was never better. A silver bowl quickly appeared in front of each cat (supplied by Saks of New York).

Gilly's was engraved with his name and the legend "Grand Winner."

Morris', of course, just said "Morris." Like Hildegarde, Ann-Margret, and Liberace, he doesn't need to identify himself any further. (Some people mistakenly spell it *Maurice*. Just remember: It's Liza with a *z* and Morris with an *s*.)

Both bowls had been heaped with a generous portion of Morris' favorite dish, tuna and egg—9-Lives, of course.

By the time Floyd, the waiter, served flaming kitty burgers en brochette as the second course, both cats had fallen into the spirit of things, ignoring the crowd that had gathered around them.

"Oh, look, how nice, Morris is taking his mother out to lunch," commented one woman.

"Is that his mistress?" another whispered to her companion.

Lunch over, Martwick put Gilly, as the amateur, into Morris' big carrying case, carried the star in the crook of his free arm, and headed off to the Chicago Bonwit Teller's and their Santa Claus, so the cats could tell him what they wanted for Christmas.

By the time we got upstairs to Santa's house, there were so many people following us that it looked as if someone were giving away free money. While we waited for the photographer to catch up, Martwick set Morris down atop his big metal kennel, in which Gilly was still incognito, staring out the bars of the little front door.

"Is that the stunt man for Morris?" asked a curious salesgirl who peered down at Gilly.

Kids who came by would stop to hug and caress Morris. "I love him," vowed one adorable little blond girl who pressed her pink cheek to his furry orange one.

"Forget it, Santa, you've been upstaged," advised a witness of the tender scene.

As the little girl left with her parents, I saw Morris look over the edge of his case to peer in at Gilly, and while he didn't say anything, I knew by the look on his face what he was thinking: "Eat your heart out, you impostor!"

"What I had more in mind was 1974
Grade A Half and Half."

"Now *that's* what I call din-din
on the fin."

Next stop on the tour was the famous Shedd Aquarium, where both cats were asked to pose atop Morris' traveling case while they viewed the panoramic wonders of the coral reef. Huge fish drifted up to stare at the cats.

Morris' tail by this time was doing a sinuous Egyptian belly dance all of its own, curling from side to side. Little by little it crept over to Gilly's side of the traveling case. Gilly seemed hypnotized by the sight of the great fish on the other side of the glass window and did not realize what was brewing.

Morris seemed to feel that he'd been a good sport so far about all this, and Martwick *had* promised him that this time he *would* talk to Morris' employers about a new mouse-flavored cat food, if he would just behave like a gentleman until this was all over.

But it was all becoming too much! What was really provoking Morris was that Gilly sat only four inches away from him; less! And regulations said anything less than twelve was war! That's what he was trying to tell this Bostonian with his tail.

"Chicken-brain!" he hissed, finally, and whopped Gilly over the head again.

"No, no, Morris," chorused absolutely everyone.

Bob Martwick quickly reminded everyone that it was time for our dinner date at the elegant Maxim's of Paris on Astor Street, where tuna was referred to as *poisson* and wine was offered by Freddie, the sommelier.

Although Gilly looked as though he'd like to find out a little more about this thing called nightclubbing, after dinner both cats went home early with Bob Martwick. Gilly would spend the next two days as a guest at Morris' Lombard home. But far away from Morris, if Martwick had anything to say about it.

On Monday the Quimbys returned home to Boston and resumed their quiet, everyday lives. I'm sure the humans breathed a sigh of relief, but I've often wondered if somewhere in the woods right now there isn't an orange tiger, practicing how to act finicky and wondering if a silver bowl is as good as a glass slipper.

A few months after Gilly's visit I was in the Pump Room again, this time with a human star, and saw Floyd, the waiter who had attended Morris and Gilly in Booth One.

"Tell me, Floyd," I asked, "was Morris a good tipper?"

"Not especially. But he behaved better than Zsa Zsa's dog," he answered with a sniff. . . .

6
"KEEP THOSE CARDS AND LETTERS COMING"

Almost from the moment he first appeared on television, Morris received so much fan mail a full-time secretary, Nancy Brady, had to be employed at 9-Lives in California to help him answer all of it.

Some of it was enough to make her blush, for it rivaled in style and content that received by any rock idol.

The most passionate mail, of course, came directly from other cats, and here, from Morris' own secret cache (where I also found six assorted rubber balls, a green-stoned cocktail ring, a gold locket, the cork from a champagne bottle, one red yarn bow from a gift package, a child's rolled-up sock, a felt toy in the shape of a hideous bug, and the label off a hair-ball medicine box showing a picture of a long-haired cat with a phone number penciled in under it), are never-before-published love letters.

> Dearest Morris: I am sending, together with this note, by my chauffeur, three cans of Iranian caviar. Let me show you how to really live.
>
> Blonde but Lonesome in
> Manhattan

"Ho-hum. Another batch of passion."

She enclosed her photo—a dreamy-looking chinchilla Persian.

Lover Boy:
   Meet me in the park at midnight.
                              Selma the Siamese in Portland

Dear Morris:
   Let me show you what jungle love is all about.
                              Princess the Panther
P.S. I am a Scorpio.

This one was written on a postcard from Lincoln Park Zoo in Chicago.

Dear Morris:
   You're the real King of Beasts as far as I'm concerned.

                              Elsa the Lioness
                              Africa

There was also a warning note from her husband in the same batch of mail!

Morris:
   You freak me out.

                              Spats with Sixtoes
                              in Ames, Iowa

Sweetie:
   On starlit nights I whisper your name to the moon,

                              Blackie
                              in Georgia

The next is obviously from a Siamese or Burmese kitty who never heard of the Women's Lib Movement, although she does take a lot of liberties:

Honorable Morris Pussycat:

Please to excuse expression of great joy. You are welcomed to my eyes as a yellow chrysanthemum in full bloom is to a thirsty bumblebee.

Permit me to introduce self. I am humble Japanese Geisha Pussycat, but have, how you say, big yen for you . . . You are welcomed to my teahouse anytime.

Bon appétit and sayonara,
Bootsie of North Miami, Florida

Jealousy constantly flashes its green eyes:

Dear Morris:

Stop seeing that white hussy or I'll scratch your eyes out.

Kitty
in Dodge City

Some were a little more reserved and ladylike:

Dear Morris:

You are my hero. You have liberated the cats of America from the "soft and purry and sleepy little kitten on the best chair" cat. We love you.

Sincerely yours,
Pussy C. Willow

But the most unusual admirer of all was revealed by a letter Morris received from the owner of a chameleon so finicky it wouldn't even eat mealworms, which are the caviar of the lizard set.

The desperate nine-year-old chameleon keeper, Carolyn Shuko of Danvers, Massachusetts, finally got an idea. She held up her chameleon to the television set while a Morris commercial was on. "It worked wonders," wrote Carolyn. "Thanks to Morris, I have a healthy, active chameleon."

A little confused, too, perhaps, but who's to criticize?

7
"EVERYTHING YOU WANTED TO KNOW
ABOUT MY PRIVATE LIFE★

★AND DARED TO ASK"

Morris is well aware that his public is clamoring for the smallest scrap of detail about his personal life, but because of his innate sense of dignity, and his inclination toward great discretion, he has been most reluctant until now to discuss it.

However, urged on by his public relations staff, his intimates, and practically everyone except his lawyers to tell everything, once and for all, and get it over with, Morris finally muttered, "Hmph! Next they'll be using a telephoto lens when I take a sunbath!" And he settled himself at the typewriter to bat out a few statements in answer to the questions most frequently asked about his private life.

Hopefully they will put at rest all those rumors about the scandals in his pre-acting days and clear up the other gossip which has made him one of the most talked-about stars of the decade. I think he has been basically honest with us, although he has wavered here and there.

How old are you, really?
   "I work out on the scratching post every day.
   "A catnip mouse makes me feel like a kitten again."
Biographer's note: Notice how with true feline eva-

siveness Morris avoids saying anything about actual years.

Bob Martwick guesses Morris was about three or four years old when he and the big orange cat crossed paths at the Hinsdale Humane Society. Which would make him about ten or eleven at this writing. Morris' personal physician goes along with this estimate.

How much do you weigh?

"You first, sweetie."

He weighs fourteen to fifteen pounds, but you don't realize how big he is until you see him, because his weight is so perfectly proportioned on his frame.

Are you a Leo?

"Leo should be so lucky as to be a Morris."

But he did hold up his head regally when he said it. A professional astrologer whom I consulted said without the exact hour and place of his birth it was hard to know for sure. But it probably is true that Morris is a Leo, as Leos love to be served, seek the best of everything, and very often enter the acting profession. She also said she thought Aquarius was his rising sign as he is so independent. He himself has often said, "Cats have a moral obligation to be independent."

What about those rumors that your roommate is a dog?

"Scurrilous," he commented, although he said it with about fifteen s's.

"I am not now nor have I ever been roommates with a dog," he denied. "A couple of them have a summer run next to mine at my country home, which is probably how *that* rumor got started, but they go their way and I go mine."

And those rumors about your not being the man you used to be?

Many people ask if, and some just assume, somewhere along the way Morris was subjected to a popular

55

"Well, it does beat riding
in the ASPCA truck."

medical operation which would remove his interest in the opposite sex.

The rumors concerning this may have been compounded when Morris didn't react to the cat that was slipped onstage as a blind date for him during his Mike Douglas Show appearance.

"Huh! What do they take me for?" said Morris. "If I went for him, I'd need more than a pair of glasses." (The other cat knew it was ridiculous too, and shamefacedly kept trying to backpedal into the wings.)

Later Bob Martwick verified that Morris' blind date was a *male* cat. It makes you wonder who was blind.

Morris' appearance on a later show in Boston, WBZ-TV (NBC), "For Women Today," left no doubts as to his interest in the opposite sex. In fact, if you were watching, you would have seen him make an absolute fool of himself over a pretty face. Another guest on the show asked Bob Martwick if it were true Morris is one of the world's most eligible bachelors. Assured that it was, the guest said he had been trying to marry off his Samantha for a long time. He went offstage a moment and brought back the sexiest, slinkiest-looking cute-kitty with a large pink bow around her neck.

Morris took one look at this feline version of Diana Ross in the adjacent chair and began a loud, plaintive meowing, almost as if he were singing a torrid love song to her over the microphone.

After a few moments of this he got up and started crossing over into her chair. A nervous show hostess almost pushed the panic button and prepared to substitute a soap ad if things got indiscreet. Bob Martwick, however, intervened and convinced Morris to act a little less impulsively (though Morris never did stop singing).

Samantha stared back at him, obviously scared out of her mind at such an overwhelming approach, but not a little interested as well.

The reports of what happened *after* the show are

vague and varied. Everybody denies everything, but rumors are the two disappeared together for three days before Martwick caught up with his charge. Further checking with the doorman at Samantha's apartment in Boston reveals she now wears, instead of the bow, a lavish rhinestone collar and that once a·month a huge truck pulls up and delivers numerous cases of assorted 9-Lives cat food. Draw your own conclusions.

Those paternity charges?

"My lawyers said to cool it on this one," said Morris, and he tucked his paws under his chest and refused to make further comment.

The truth is there very well could be a number of Morris Jrs. and even Grand Jrs. running around as a result of the reckless life our star led in his pre-acting days. But no one can be sure who they are or where they might be.

Still, occasionally an irate cat owner calls the Chicago ad agency that makes the Morris commercials, accuses Morris of getting his cat pregnant, and threatens a paternity suit.

At this point account execs turn out performances of diplomacy which would make Henry Kissinger stay home forever. They explain that because of Morris' incalculable worth as a star, he is never out of anyone's sight for a minute. And that, besides, Morris has never been in Idaho. It must have been a cat who just looked like Morris.

Having an heir is becoming more and more a consideration with Morris, however. Left to his own devices, he would probably continue his playboy ways. But he knows there must be someone who will continue to spread the gospel of finickiness throughout the land.

There's nobody special as yet, or so he says. As for Ethel, the white Persian with whom he's co-starred in a couple of commercials, he snorted, "Ridiculous! Absolutely ridiculous!" Ethel, called long distance at her summer home in Amagansett, mewed, "We're friends, just friends."

The very latest rumor as we go to press is that after a close call—a studio-arranged romance on the West Coast that began to get serious, but then fizzled because she wanted a career of her own and didn't want a family—Morris is holding out for a harem. This is driving his whole staff bananas, as they wonder how it's going to look in print, but Morris read somewhere about Frazier the lion and keeps arguing, "If *he* can do it . . ."

What kind of kitty puts a wiggle in your whiskers?

Officially Morris wishes to remain noncommittal about this as he feels if he says he likes one type, it will hurt a lot of feelings, and frankly he grooves on all that adoration.

Off the record, however, after observing his reactions over the years, it can be said he will always stop and look at a white Persian.

As for real companionship, he seems to lean toward the type of kitty that is dainty, athletic and quick, and can do a lot of the things which because of his sheer size he finds difficult to do. For example, treading across the top of a shower curtain bar. I think he finds these displays slightly threatening, but very exciting.

Once a besotted owner played Dolly Levi and wrote Morris a matchmaking letter, describing as one of her kitty's virtues the ability "to knock off any 10-lb. dog." Morris read *this* with a great deal of whisker wiggling as he does find such qualities admirable. He says he goes for the spitfire type.

Morris thinks Siamese girls talk too much and they bore him with all their mindless chatter.

One story published in *TV Guide* said that with a little imagination you could easily picture Morris shoving a grapefruit half into a Siamese's face, the way James

59

Cagney did to Mae Clarke in the movie *The Public Enemy*. This, if you know Morris at all, is far, far from the truth.

It is much more likely the Siamese would squash the grapefruit half in *his* face, after she'd heard some of the things he'd say to her!

Can you explain your relationship with Jacqueline Susann?

"I have never met her, but I understand she is a great admirer of mine," says Morris. However, he denies that her roman à clef novel, *Once Is Not Enough*, refers in the title to his own nine lives.

As for other humans in his past, Bob Martwick says, "He's so warm with people, there had to be somebody!" But this is one thing I can never get Morris to say the first thing about. Repeated questioning will only send him off in a huff, so there's no way to pursue it.

Do you sleep with anything on?

"Just with a paw across my eyes."

On a waterbed?

"No. One careless claw and it's floodsville."

Will you talk about the affairs you had before you were famous?

Unfortunately, the rumors that Morris was picked up by the Hindsdale Humane Society truck because he was keeping several families up nights while he was romancing their lady cats are true. In fact, the Humane Society had been getting calls about him for some time and were aware he was around in the neighborhood, but he moved so frequently and was such a big operator, it took a while before they could get a bead on him.

Morris himself is mum on the whole thing, so we scouted around his old neighborhood and, after numer-

"Not vichyssoise *again!*"

ous false leads, met up with someone who did know him from the old days, a pretty calico-and-white who was perched on the banister of her back porch.

"Do I remember him!" she exclaimed. She was just a kitten then herself, but she'd seen him around a couple of times and she'd certainly heard a lot about him. "Snnff!" she said. "If that's who he was, do you know he was the talk of the neighborhood even then for his smooth lines? Do you know his favorite was, 'Hey, glitter-eyes, come down to the park and let's watch the grasshopper races'?" (I'm afraid that does sound a lot like Morris.)

Anyway, the calico wasn't there herself, but she remembers the gossip down by the garbage cans was that the orange cat, never one for being shy, liked to jump onto picture-window ledges of an evening and peer in to see if the lady cat resident would care to go for a stroll.

Very unfortunately, the evening he picked to look in the window of an elderly widow who lived alone with an attractive, sultry-looking black Persian (with whom he'd had a tête-à-tête at her screen door earlier that afternoon), the woman was watching an old vampire movie on the late, late show. Just when the vampire was lurking about the castle, this orange cat materialized out of the dark onto the window ledge and switched on his infrared, high-beam eyesight so he could see.

Well, the black Persian told this calico later that "even when I caught my claw in the drapes and hung there, I never screamed so hard."

The next morning our Lothario was taken down to the station and booked. Of course we'll never know if it was Morris this all happened to, but it seems as likely a story as any.

Since the opposite sex was almost literally the end of him, Morris takes a much more cautious attitude today and has a much more mature outlook when it comes to romance.

8
"I COME BETWEEN DYAN CANNON AND BURT REYNOLDS"

Early in 1972 our feline friend got it into his head to have a fling at another medium, a full-length motion picture.

He was offered a starring role in a Robert M. Weitman production for Columbia Pictures called *Shamus,* the title being slang for a police detective or a private investigator.

The producer and director had already signed up America's favorite foldout fantasy, that *Cosmopolitan* man, Burt Reynolds, for the leading human role of McCoy when the script and contract hit the mailbox at Morris' luxury estate.

It was a story line to which our hero could really relate. Reynolds, as McCoy, leads a kind of roving alley-cat existence himself as a private detective who fleshes out a meager income as a pool parlor hustler and has his lair in a large garbage can of an apartment, with a pool table as a bed.

It goes without saying he was well-cast in the part with his roguish charm, his lithe, tigerish walk, his air of being ready to explode if rubbed the wrong way, and not least, his ability not to take himself too seriously, almost to parody himself on the screen.

Pauline Kael, the *New Yorker* movie critic, summed

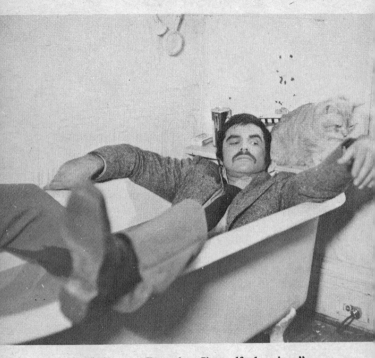

"I'd join you, Burt, but I'm self-cleaning."
Credit: *"Shamus"—A Columbia Pictures
Presentation of a Robert M. Weitman Production*

it up when she called Burt Reynolds "a swinger Clark Gable."

With that, you begin to get the picture why our four-footed superstar would be inclined to put his famous paw print on the dotted line of the *Shamus* contract.

It held a soul brothers kind of attraction for him. If the original King had already passed on to that Great Movie Set in the sky, Morris thought it would be amusing to do a number with his contemporary equivalent; they would be counter-symbolic of each other: Burt Reynolds, sex symbol and neo-Clark Gable of the human world, and Morris, the same in feline circles.

The first day out on the shooting schedule in the Red Hook section of Brooklyn, a police-estimated crowd of three thousand, mostly women and children, nearly rioted when Reynolds appeared on the scene. (Morris says actually they were there to see him, and the crowd only rioted when they had to take Reynolds as second-best.)

Reynolds, who insists on doing his own stunts (he is an Aquarian and very independent, like someone else we know; the parallels pile up), goes through some real tussling with three Great Danes, police dogs from the kennels of an ex-U.S. Army Canine Corps chief, Capt. Arthur Haggarty. The Danes are guard dogs for a rich, mystery-shrouded recluse, who is Reynolds' client, and when the shamus tries to see him, the dogs attack him.

Then Reynolds/McCoy comes home and gets smacked around by some thugs.

As he sprawls there on the floor, he takes the worst beating of all, as far as the cameras go, from our hero, who, once on the set, immediately took it upon himself to expand his role as "Cat."

Morris' first scene in *Shamus* called for his entrance into the room in which Reynolds is lying out cold on the floor after being worked over by bad guys.

Morris licks Reynolds' face and brings him around

to consciousness. Whereupon the private eye staggers into the bathroom where he runs water into the tub and then collapses into it, with a mighty splash, still fully clothed. All of which Morris and Reynolds perform in a single take.

That's as far as Morris' part in that scene was written into the script. But trust our orange-furred friend to seize the opportunity and ham things up.

As Reynolds soaked soggily in the tub, Morris unexpectedly leaped onto its rim to gaze down on Burt's sprawled body with his crooked but somewhat sympathetic grin, as if to say, "Boy, you can't stay out of trouble, can you? Well, I've been there, too."

The additional footage was kept in by the delighted director.

It is obvious that Cat is important to McCoy. The shamus worries about his orange tiger friend and wants to make sure he gets a square meal when he shows up in the fire escape window. He gives explicit instructions to his first girl friend in the film to watch for Cat and to give him a can of his favorite brand of food. She is not too enthused, so it is no surprise when Burt drops her, fast.

Dyan Cannon, as Alexis, one of the other women he takes up with, is a much better choice as she is very sympathetic to Cat. In fact, Cat shows up when she's around, which he didn't do when the other gal was there, which says something in itself.

The sympathies apparently were no act. When asked how she liked working with our feline superstar, Dyan Cannon replied: "Morris is the most attentive co-star I've ever worked with."

As for Burt, he was big enough to admit he'd met a real challenge: "I found Morris to be the most unselfish actor I've ever worked with in terms of the camera, but when it came to love scenes he was awfully selfish, I felt, and concentrated on his own gratification. However, that alone would probably make him a star."

Burt is referring to the grand larceny Morris com-

"Not *that* again."
Credit: *"Shamus"*—*A Columbia Pictures Presentation of a Robert M. Weitman Production*

mitted in the love scene with Dyan. It was something no Hollywood authority would think possible, what with the high-voltage teaming of Burt and Dyan.

The two were smooching it up when Morris strolled in and sat between them on the pool table where it was all happening.

Dyan takes a perceptive look at Cat, who sits there long enough to be a boulder in the path of progress.

"He looks like you," she says to Reynolds/McCoy.

"Yeh!" says Burt. (I wonder who writes his lines.)

Then Morris lifts his head disdainfully and makes his exit with an expression which clearly says, "Cripes, I could do better than that!"

You can see why Reynolds was rueful.

Recently Morris received another film offer, a role in *The Long Goodbye,* as adapted from the Raymond Chandler book of the same name. This one would star Elliot Gould as another private detective who lives a scroungy, loner kind of existence.

Morris turned the part down.

He didn't want to be typecast.

9
"MY LIFE-STYLE AT HOME, FOR THOSE OF YOU WHO FEAR I MIGHT BE EXPLOITED BY CROOKED MANAGERS"

One of the questions most frequently asked about Morris concerns his homelife.

Some of his fans, suspecting the worst of human nature, voice a worry that when he is off camera he is kept locked up in a dreary cage somewhere, alone and unloved.

Yet there are still others who go to the opposite extreme and fantasize that he is kept in a large pink bower, that he is fanned by slaves and pampered like a sultan. They imagine him fed on peeled grapes and Perrier water and never allowed to set his pink-padded feet upon the ground.

The truth, as it often does, lies somewhere in between.

Morris lives the life of any normal cat, we are happy to say, with a few extras thrown in.

Home for Morris is a luxurious kennel on an idyllically beautiful six-and-a-half-acre parcel of land in a suburb west of Chicago. The place is a slice of California—low buildings, lots of trees, and out in the back a large pond where Canadian geese occasionally skitter across the surface like skipped stones—a true feline Howard Hughes hideaway for our superstar.

This modern kennel specializes in grooming and

"Now, what was the number of that cute
little tabby I met in Toronto?"

"How boring! Every time I get a new chauffeur, he manages to get us lost."

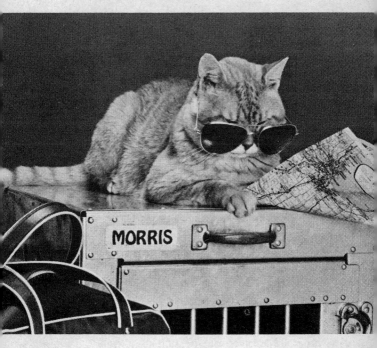

obedience training for dogs (even a star has to put up with some crosses in real life). Bob Martwick and a man named Stuart Schroder are partners in the business, but they agree the place got its real proprietor the day Morris first walked in the door.

"He thinks he owns the place," snorts Martwick, and it is obvious to others, too, that like many human stars, our Mr. Finicky considers himself a businessman when he is offstage.

During the day Morris takes his business responsibilities seriously. He goes anyplace he wants to within the kennels and he does a good job of overseeing it. Often he sits in a window and scrutinizes the dogs as they arrive. Or he keeps watch from the receptionist's desk to make sure everything is flowing in good order.

"Around here we call him 'The King,'" says the office manager, on whose desk Morris sometimes sits: "The King, that's what he is," she laughs.

Indeed, it seems that of all names Morris prefers that title best.

"He challenges every dog," says Martwick. "He won't move an inch. He has swatted many a customer's dog in the nose."

Which cannot be good business tactics for an owner to use, but somehow it works in the way perhaps snob appeal and haughty maître d's do in certain restaurants.

Although there are up to sixteen fellow actor cats in residence at the kennels, "he won't tolerate cats either," says Martwick. However, he is *always* interested if they are girls.

Morris loves the outdoors, but he is never allowed outside alone. When he does go for a stroll it's always with some strong-arm bodyguard, if not Martwick himself.

Nor is he allowed out in inclement weather when he could easily catch a cold. In the summertime, however, he gets to loll about in a covered run under huge shade trees.

One way Morris keeps fit is to take a break, or even several breaks throughout a hectic business day, and indulge in a snooze. Right under his desk is a furry red rug that he likes (like many bachelors, his taste in home furnishings is somewhat garish).

Martwick had also gotten him a bed, "but he paid no attention to it."

At night Morris goes upstairs with Martwick to an apartment over the kennels. Morris has his own bed there, too, but "he prefers to sleep on the foot of my bed, a chair, or wherever he feels like it," says Martwick.

When he and Martwick are touring together, it's not easy for Morris to forget the old days, I guess, and one of the first things he does in a new hotel room is to dump over the wastebasket and see what might be in it. Then he checks out the whole room to make sure there are no dogs or mice lurking about. After he's assured himself, he decides on one spot as his very own, whether it's an easy chair or the foot of the bed, and there he settles down.

As with any creative individual, however, sometimes jet lag or people lag catches up with him, he reverts to his natural habits, and night becomes day.

Martwick has a few anecdotes to tell about lamps crashing over in the middle of the night, or being awakened out of a sound sleep by fourteen pounds of orange tiger using Martwick's chest as a heliport, as Morris springs from a tall dresser.

Morris usually gets out of such embarrassing social situations by using, once again, that crooked grin.

Although Morris is probably the only cat in the world to be owned by a conglomerate, just about everyone in the latter is flattered to think of him as a personal friend, and there is a constant concern for his happiness.

If it were not so, he could always go off and be a houseguest of the Shah of Iran, or cruise on the Onassis yacht. You can be sure he gets plenty of invitations.

But in his opinion, be it ever so humble and surrounded by dogs, there's no place like your own furry red rug.

10
"WHY I THINK THERE SHOULD BE A CAT IN THE WHITE HOUSE"

Show-business figures today find that the political arena is very often a natural progression from superstardom.

Why should Morris be any exception?

As a star he has certainly had great sociological impact. He has been able to restore catdom to its rightful exalted position, in a manner not seen since the ancient days of Egypt.

Another very satisfying accomplishment is that the human male can now stop being a closet cat freak and is able to express freely his admiration for the feline species without being considered some kind of sissy. Until now, even male veterinarians have had to be careful about confessing their interest.

While Morris has a definite social conscience in regard to his own kind, and is very forward-looking in some human areas, he is absolutely hopeless in others.

Once when I asked him for a statement on Women's Lib, he told me, "I think we should let them do whatever they want to, as long as they are home to run the can opener when we are hungry."

Although reporters have been very uninhibited about asking him almost every other kind of question in interviews which have appeared in the major news-

"Hmph! How much clearer do I have to
make it that Any Cat Can?"

papers of the country (he made the front page of the *Christian Science Monitor,* the centerfold of the *National Inquirer,* and *Variety* once wrote him up in its own peculiar style), no one has been perceptive enough to inquire of his political ambitions.

And indeed they do exist, as he admits here for the first time in print.

He says he would very much like to see, before this one of his nine lives is over, a cat in the White House.

There has not been one since John F. Kennedy was President and allowed his children to keep Tom Kitten, a mischievous striped fellow, as their pet in the residential quarters of the White House.

I haven't caught Morris out "stumping" yet, but he did a lot of indignant hmph!-ing at newspaper stories about a certain red setter wolfing down birthday cake at a White House party. (If there is anything Morris can't stand, as we all know, it's an indiscriminate eater.)

This was followed by some muttering about the "right image."

Once I even heard Morris say there wouldn't be any "bugs" in the White House if a cat lived there.

He believes he could run himself on an "unbought and unbossed" slogan; and who else can you say that about these days?

He feels very strongly that "finickiness should become a national virtue."

I can just see Morris now, roaming majestically down those historic halls, stopping to sniff at a Williamsburg reproduction, and dropping in to sit on Henry Kissinger's state papers, while Henry laments not being "top dog" any longer.

All of this is not as farfetched as you may think it is. Morris already has come close to being called by popular demand into public service and is already representing, at least symbolically, his species and all it stands for in highest government circles.

In November, 1973, Sir Robert Jackson, an Under-Secretary-General of the U.N., wrote to Star-Kist Foods, the company which owns 9-Lives, asking for a color photo of "world-famous Morris" to put on the wall of his office both for his own edification and that of his smitten staff. The photo was dispatched from California to New York, and in January, 1974, Sir Robert replied:

"I have just returned to the headquarters of the United Nations, and was delighted to be greeted by Morris, who has on his face a look of superb confidence which I only wish could permeate all those who have responsibilities within the United Nations for dealing with international problems!

"Possibly the best answer would be to recommend to the General Assembly that they should give serious consideration to appointing Morris to some very senior position; he would be a natural to direct a United Nations organization for protecting animals!

". . . all of us in the U.N. feel much happier to have Morris to inspire us with his attitude of complete confidence. . . ."

So you see, Morris' natural leadership abilities could very well at some time in this life, or in the next, lead him to a distinguished career in world affairs.

Could he possibly have this in mind himself for a future life?

Whether cats have any control or not over how they will be spending each of their lives is not clear.

Morris does not seem to spend much time pondering it, as he keeps busy enjoying the rewards brought from his present duties as idol to a nation's cats.

In fact, I think one of the high points of his whole career occurred not so long ago when he returned one afternoon to the village of Hinsdale. Although it is but a few miles geographically from his home, of course the historic distance he has traveled from one to the other is immeasurable.

The occasion was "Be Kind to Animals" week, and Morris had been invited to speak to the children at a Hinsdale school on the subject.

Morris was quite animated and on his toes that day at the school, almost as if he were expecting to see someone special there among the children. Usually, you know, he puts on the big, bored movie-star act.

Apparently, however, he did not see whoever it was he might have been looking for, and as he left, Martwick thought he seemed a little disgruntled.

To cheer him a bit, after the school program Martwick decided to stop a few blocks away at the Hinsdale animal shelter where years ago it had all begun for Morris.

It was a historic, touching occasion as everyone stopped what he was doing to watch the star return again to this place that held so much meaning for him.

There, in the Kitty Room, as a matter of fact, at right angles to the tier of little cages, is a framed photo of Morris that is hung from the bare cement-block walls. It shows Morris sitting, most correctly, at a table in a fine restaurant. There is a "reserved" card on the red-checked tablecloth.

That photo is so placed that any cat in the cages can see it and be inspired by it.

One of the *paparazzi* who is always following Morris around when he is out in public happened to be tagging along just then, and everyone thought it would make a great gag shot to put Morris back in the cage where he was discovered. . . .

"Hmph! Some sense of humor," he grumped, but went along with it, I suspect for his own reasons.

As the photographer aimed his camera, a very young kitten who was doing time in the next cage recognized Morris for who he really was. The little one peeked out and up as far as he could for a better look, with a breathless "Gee, I wish I could grow up to be just like you" expression.

Of course, Morris couldn't say it aloud—the old image and all that—but I knew he was going to give the little guy his first lesson in how to get where *he* wanted to go, and the look on his face clearly said it:

"Hmph! Little dum-dum hasn't learned yet that every cat is a star!"

"I like you. You're cute . . . a little *weird,*
but cute."

MORRIS' MEMORY BOOK

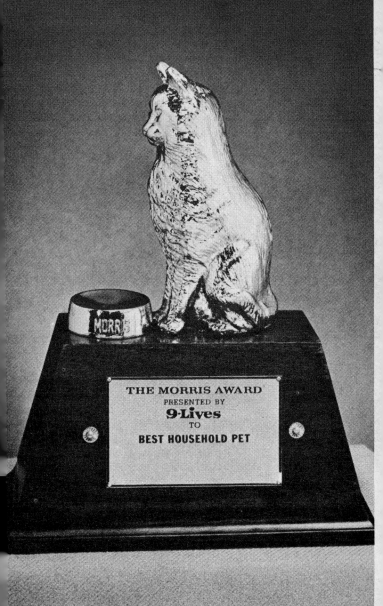

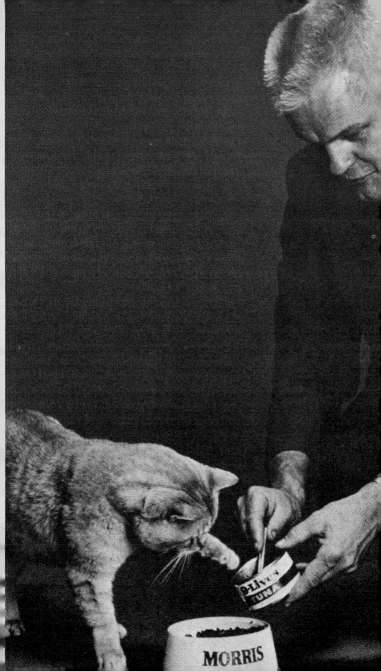

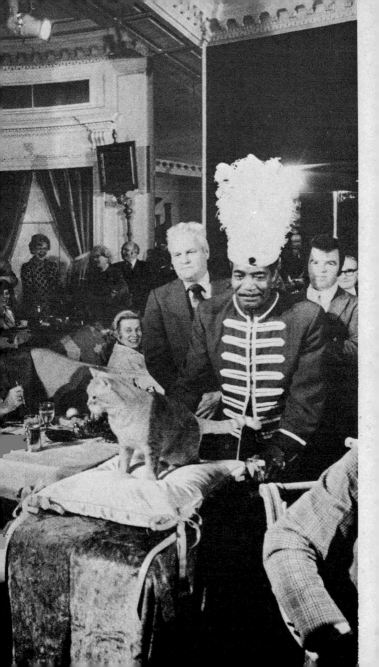